②

Nancy®

Sometimes I
do my homework,
and sometimes
it does me.

by Jerry Scott

A TRUM

Published by The Trumpet Club
666 Fifth Avenue, New York, New York 10103

NANCY Comic Strips Copyright © 1989, 1990
United Feature Syndicate, Inc.

ISBN: 0-440-84377-4

Printed in the United States of America
February 1991
10 9 8 7 6 5 4 3 2 1
OPM

BRUSH! BRUSH! BRUSH!

OK, YOU WERE RIGHT... IT **IS** TOO DEEP FOR SLEDDING

TOLD YOU.

JERRY SCOTT

© 1989 United Feature Syndicate, Inc.

THIS CRUSH YOU HAVE ON THE SUBSTITUTE TEACHER IS GETTING ON MY NERVES

JERRY SCOTT

SSSCHLORP!

SSSCHLORP!

I GUESS SOME PEOPLE CAN WEAR PIGTAILS, AND SOME CAN'T

If you had six pieces of candy, and three of your friends asked you to give each of them one...

...how many would you have left?

Friends or candy?

ESSAY QUESTION

What do you want to be when you grow up, and why?

Boss of the universe.

Because I said so.

I CAN'T BELIEVE THAT WE HAVE TO COME TO SCHOOL ON A DAY LIKE THIS!

IT'S **FREEZING**! IT'S **MISERABLE**! IT'S TOTALLY BARBARIC TO FORCE CHILDREN TO ENDURE WEATHER LIKE THIS!

SO HOW LONG UNTIL RECESS?

JERRY SCOTT

RIINNGGG!

YO! NANCY'S SCHOOL YEAR RAP-UP

WHEN WE STARTED LAST **FALL**, NOBODY WAS A **FOOL**! WE KNEW EXACTLY WHAT WE COULD EXPECT FROM **SCHOOL**!

BOOK REVIEWS! **QUIZZES**! HOMEWORK OVER**LOAD**! SOMETIMES WE THOUGHT OUR BRAINS MIGHT JUST **EXPLODE**

BUT WE LEARNED A LOT OF **STUFF**, MAKE NO **MISTAKE**... ESPECIALLY IN THE CLASSES WHERE WE STAYED **AWAKE**!

CONTINUED...

YO!

NANCY'S SCHOOL YEAR RAP-UP!

NOW SCHOOL IS **OVER**, THE YEAR HAS **PASSED** NOW IT'S SUMMERTIME — I'M TALKIN' MAJOR **CONTRAST!**

WOOKA! WOOKA! WOU!

NO MORE **PENCIL!** NO MORE **BOOK!** NO MORE CLASSES, BUT DON'T GET **SHOOK**...

IT'S VACATION **TIME** WE ALL **AGREE.** SO JUST RELAX AND LET YOUR BRAIN BEGIN TO **ATROPHY!**

JERRY SCOTT